CONTENTS

* Color transparencies are found at the back of this book. Each transparency should be used to introduce the corresponding unit.

TEACHING GUIDE

Page 1 *FOOD GUIDE PYRAMID*

CONCEPT: The Food Guide Pyramid is a guide for consumers to aid them in making the best daily food choices. It helps meal planners provide a diet that is low in fats and sugars.

BACKGROUND INFORMATION: In 1992, the United States Department of Agriculture published the *Dietary Guidelines for Americans*. Accompanying the guidelines was the Food Guide Pyramid. Research had shown that many people were not making healthy food choices and had insufficient information to plan diets that were correct for their daily needs. Typical diets were high in saturated fats and also high in sugars and sodium. The health problems associated with high cholesterol diets are well documented. The Food Guide Pyramid provides an easy reference for making healthy daily food choices that are appropriate for a person's age and activity level. Similar to the historical basic food groups, the Food Pyramid also categorizes foods into groups and gives the recommended numbers of servings per day. The pyramid shape emphasizes that the largest number of servings each day should come from the Bread, Cereal, Rice, and Pasta Group. This group provides a number of nutrients needed for good health. It is also low in fat. A variety of fruits and vegetables are needed to supply the body with vitamins and minerals. The Milk and Meat Groups are important sources of protein and other essential nutrients. The apex of the pyramid emphasizes that fats, oils, and sugars should be used only sparingly.

ENRICHMENT ACTIVITIES:
1) Milk has been referred to as the "perfect food." Why do some people disagree with this?
2) Find out about the nutritional value of condiments.

ANSWER KEY:
Page 1–Transparency
1) Bread Group; Fats, Oils, and Sweets Group
2) Fruit and Bread Groups

Study Question: Answers will vary but should show some servings from each group. Example: bread, banana, milk, margarine, scrambled eggs with green peppers.

Page 1a
1) A. Fats, Oils, and Sweets—use sparingly
   B. Milk, Yogurt, and Cheese—2–3 servings
   C. Vegetables—3–5 servings
   D. Meat, Poultry, Fish, Dry Beans, Eggs, and Nuts—2–3 servings
   E. Fruit—2–4 servings
   F. Bread, Cereal, Rice, and Pasta—6–11 servings
2) Milk and Fruit Groups
3) a. F, b. B, c. E, d. D, e. F, f. C, g. C, h. D, i. E, j. C, k. E, l. B, m. D, n. D, o. F

Page 1b
1) **Rice**—China, India, Japan, Vietnam, Burma, Thailand;
   Corn—United States, Brazil, Argentina, China, Mexico, Africa;
   Wheat—United States, Canada, Argentina, Australia, Russia, France;
   Meat—United States, Canada, Argentina, Australia, England, Russia;
   Fish—United States, Russia, China, Peru, Japan, South Korea
2) barley, oats, rye, sorghum
3) United States, China, Russia
4) rice, fish, corn, wheat, meat

Page 2 *THE BREAD, CEREAL, RICE, AND PASTA GROUP*

CONCEPT: The Bread Group is the base of the Food Guide Pyramid and is an important source of energy–producing foods and vitamins for the body.

BACKGROUND INFORMATION: Bread has often been called the "staff of life." Bread is a baked mixture of liquids—water and/or milk—and the flour of a cereal grain—wheat, rye, or corn. A loaf of white bread contains a large amount of carbohydrates, proteins, minerals, and vitamins. Wheat, converted to flour, is found in many products such as crackers, doughnuts, pancakes, pie crusts, cakes, bagels, pretzels, and pastas—spaghetti, noodles, macaroni. Rice is the staple food in many Asian countries and is also a favorite grain in the United States. Other grains used for food include barley, oats, and sorghum. The proteins, minerals, and vitamins found in these grain–cereal foods replenish worn–out body cells with necessary nutrients. Dry cereals with milk, and fruits or fruit juices comprise a good breakfast for young people.

ENRICHMENT ACTIVITIES:

1) Find out about the action of yeast in the bread–making process. Use iodine to test foods for the presence of starch. A drop of iodine on a piece of cracker will produce a black or purple spot confirming a starch is present.
   Safety Note: Use precautions with iodine.

ANSWER KEY:
Page 2–Transparency
1) rolls, pretzels, crackers, waffles, pancakes, tortillas
2) breads, cereals, waffles, pancakes, bagels.

Study Question: Examples: Irish soda bread, Swedish limpa, Norwegian flatbread, German pumpernickel, Syrian/Greek pita, French bread

Page 2a
1) pies, doughnuts, cakes, cookies
2) potato chips, tangerine, raisins
3) carbohydrates, fats, proteins, minerals, vitamins A, B, and E
4) spaghetti, macaroni, mostaccioli, noodles
5) This group has many nutrients, but is low in saturated fats and sugars.

Page 3 *THE FRUIT GROUP*

CONCEPT: The Fruit Group provides the body with carbohydrates, fiber, and vitamins A and C. Fresh fruits are low in fats and sodium.

BACKGROUND INFORMATION: Two to four servings from this food group are recommended for each day. Fresh fruits are an important source of carbohydrates (mostly fruit sugars) and fiber. Fiber is a healthy element for the diet as it provides bulk that helps the large intestine form and remove wastes from the body. Fruits are also a major source of vitamins A and C. Vitamin A promotes growth, healthy skin, and good eyesight. Vitamin C, found in citrus fruits, is essential for growth, the healing of wounds, and for maintaining healthy bones and teeth. Fruits are low in saturated fats and in sodium and they are an excellent component of a good diet. All fruits can be eaten fresh. Some are canned and others are dried. Others are often made into juices for refreshing, healthful drinks. Biologists define a fruit as the edible, pulpy mass that covers the seeds of certain plants and trees. Technically, this would include such structures as tomatoes, peppers, cucumbers, string beans, and squash. However, in commerce these fruits are labeled as vegetables.

ENRICHMENT ACTIVITIES:

1) Find out about these types of fruits and give an example of each: legume, drupe, berry, akene, and pome.
2) Find out about the fruits of these trees: maple, elm, ash, oak, and walnut. Are any of these fruits edible?

ANSWER KEY:
Page 3–Transparency
1) oranges, lemons, limes, grapefruits
2) Almost all fruits can be served as a dessert—fruit bowls, fruit with ice cream, and in pies.

Study Question: Biologists classify fruits as those structures with a pulpy mass covering the seeds of herbaceous plants and trees. Vegetable is a non–technical term and has come to mean the edible, non–fruit structures. However, a number of "vegetables" are actually fruits.

Page 3a
1) A. strawberries, B. watermelon and can-

taloupe, C. orange, D. grapefruit,
E. bananas, F. apples, G. pear, H. grapes,
I. blueberries, J. raspberries (or blackberries), K. peach, L. lemons

2) **trees**—apples, oranges, bananas, peaches, pears, plums, lemons, limes, grapefruit;
bushes—raspberries, cranberries, blueberries, blackberries;
vines—grapes, cantaloupe, watermelon, strawberries

3) **pies**—apples, peaches, plums, strawberries, raspberries, blueberries, blackberries;
jellies—apples, oranges, grapes, peaches, plums, strawberries, raspberries, blueberries, blackberries;
juices—oranges, grapes, lemons, limes, grapefruits, all berries

4) Examples: cherries, apricots, nectarines, kiwis, pineapples

Page 4 *THE VEGETABLE GROUP*

CONCEPT: The Vegetable Group provides the body with carbohydrates, minerals, and vitamins A, B, C, E, and K. Fresh vegetables are low in fat.

BACKGROUND INFORMATION: Three to five daily servings are recommended from this food group for a healthy diet. Fresh vegetables supply the body with carbohydrates (starches and sugars), a number of minerals, and a variety of vitamins, enabling the body to maintain its healthy functioning. Vegetables may be cooked, baked, or eaten raw. The proper preparation of vegetables is important, because their nutritional value can be lost in the cooking process. Generally, the longer a food is cooked, the greater the loss of nutrients. Vegetables are an important source of fiber. As with fruits, vegetables often have a high percentage of water, an important component of a good diet. Many people in less developed countries have insufficient protein in their diets. Some vegetables are high in protein and can supply this nutrient. The winged bean, grown and used in the Pacific islands and Southeast Asia, is protein–rich and could be cultivated in countries requiring high–protein foods.

ENRICHMENT ACTIVITIES:
1) Find out about the fiber content of vegetables such as potatoes, celery, spinach, and pumpkin.
2) Find out how freezing vegetables helps to retain their nutritional value.

ANSWER KEY:
Page 4–Transparency
1) Above—corn, lettuce, spinach, cucumbers, broccoli, asparagus, beans, tomatoes, peas, peppers; Below—potatoes, carrots, radishes, beets
2) Examples: lima beans, cabbage, cauliflower, celery, collards, onions, pumpkins, turnips, eggplant, squash, artichoke, zucchini

Study Question: The winged bean presently being grown in and used in the Phillipines, other Pacific islands, and parts of Asia is a protein–rich legume. The leaves, tendrils, bean pods, seeds, and roots can all be eaten. Because of its many edible plant parts, the winged bean has been referred to as a "supermarket on a stalk."

Page 4a
1) A. corn, B. beet, C. potatoes, D. radishes, E. asparagus, F. spinach, G. carrots, H. broccoli, I. cucumber, J. peppers, K. peas, L. lettuce, M. tomatoes, N. green beans, O. lettuce
2) carbohydrates, minerals, and vitamins A, B, C, E, and K
3) **roots**—carrots, radishes, beets;
stems—asparagus, potatoes (tuber);
leaves—lettuce, spinach;
flowers—broccoli and cauliflower;
seeds—corn, peas
Note: Cucumbers, peppers, and tomatoes are fruits of their plants.
4) Starch—potatoes, beans, corn, sweet potatoes; Fiber—potatoes, asparagus, carrots, broccoli, spinach

Page 5 *THE MILK, YOGURT, AND CHEESE GROUP*

CONCEPT: The Milk, Yogurt, and Cheese Group supplies the body with carbohydrates, fats, proteins, minerals (calcium and phosphorous), and vitamins A, B, D, and E.

BACKGROUND INFORMATION: The Food Guide Pyramid recommends that 2–3 servings from this group be eaten daily. Often referred to as the dairy group, the Milk, Yogurt, and Cheese Group provides the body with carbohydrates, fats, and proteins. The minerals calcium and phosphorus are essential for bone and tooth development and muscle activity. This food group also supplies vitamins A, B, D, and E. Vitamins A and B are involved in body growth. Vitamin D is responsible for the absorption of calcium and phosphorus. There are few foods with significant amounts of this vitamin. Cow's milk is not a good source; however, it is enriched or fortified to ensure a content of 400 units of vitamin D per quart of milk. Vitamin E stabilizes cell membranes and protects red blood cells. Another dairy product is butter. It is made by separating cream from the milk and then churning the cream. Margarine, often used as a substitute for butter, is made from skim milk and vegetable oils. There are two other types of milk products: fermented milk and cheese. Treating milk with microorganisms produces buttermilk, sour cream, or yogurt. Milk that is coagulated by microorganisms, by the enzyme rennin, or a combination of both processes produces a semi–solid or solid food called cheese. Microorganisms inoculated into the curd give the various kinds of cheeses their distinct flavors.

ENRICHMENT ACTIVITIES:
1) Find out about the source of the enzyme rennin and the early manufacture of cheese.
2) Find out about the role of seaweed in the manufacturing of ice cream.

ANSWER KEY:
Page 5–Transparency
1) A dairy is a place where milk is stored and made into butter and cheese. The term "dairy products" refers to milk and the many food items made from it.
2) The minerals calcium and phosphorus found in milk group products are necessary for bone formation, growth, and repair.

Study Question: Pasteurization destroys disease–producing bacteria and checks activity of fermentation bacteria; homogenization is a process that finely divides fat particles in milk and emulsifies those particles so that the cream does not separate and rise to the top of the milk container.

Page 5a
1) A. cream, B. yogurt, C. sour cream, D. butter, E. cottage cheese, F. cheese, G. margarine, H. milk
2) popsicle, banana, eggs, orange juice, salad oil, tofu
3) carbohydrates, fats, proteins, minerals, vitamins
4) By selecting low–fat substitutes such as skim milk, ice milk, and low–fat yogurt.

Page 6 *THE MEAT, POULTRY, FISH, DRY BEANS, EGGS, AND NUTS GROUP*

CONCEPT: This group provides the body with proteins, fats, minerals, and vitamins B, D, and E. Avoid eating high–fat meats.

BACKGROUND INFORMATION: Two or three servings from this group are recommended for each day. The Meat Group provides the major portion of our daily protein requirements. Proteins are necessary for growth and for the replacement and repair of cells. Fats, in limited amounts, are required for energy, cushioning organs, and the absorption of some vitamins. The fat content of meats varies considerably depending on the cut and grade of the meat and the type of animal from which it comes. Minerals and vitamins from this group are important for growth and healthy cell activities. Many meats are good sources of iron and the B vitamins. Meat sources include the flesh from cows, pigs, sheep, and poultry (chickens, ducks, turkeys). Also included in this food group are the various forms of seafood—fish, shrimp, oysters, clams, squid, and scallops. Some fish contain large amounts of vitamin A. Other foods such as dry peas, beans, lentils, eggs, nuts and peanut butter are included in the meat group because of their relatively high amounts of the nutrient protein. Most meats are sold fresh, but they can be smoked, canned, frozen or cured with salt to preserve their freshness.

ENRICHMENT ACTIVITIES:
1) Find out about the history of making sausages.
2) Find out about the various cuts of meats such as chuck, brisket, loin, round, and flank.

ANSWER KEY:
Page 6–Transparency
1) vitamins B, D, and E
2) Examples: squid, buffalo, shark, game animals

Study Question: The soybean has been used to make a type of milk, cooking oil, shortening, salad oil, and artificial meats.

Page 6a
1) a. pig, b. cow, c. pig, d. chicken, e. calf, f. pig, g. cow, h. cow and pig, i. sheep, j. cow or pig
2) chicken, duck, turkey
3) b, c, d, g, h, j, k, l
4) proteins, fats, minerals, vitamins B, D, and E

Page 7 *FATS, OILS, AND SWEETS*

CONCEPT: This food group mainly provides the body with fats and carbohydrates. Foods in this group should be eaten sparingly.

BACKGROUND INFORMATION: Fats, oils, and sweets are not harmful unless eaten in amounts greater than the body can healthfully utilize. They are often very appetizing. Fats are chemical compounds that are insoluble in water and are solid at room temperatures. Oils are fats in liquid form at 20° C. Fats and oils are the most concentrated sources of energy in the foods we eat. They come from both animal and plant sources. Fats are either saturated or unsaturated. Saturated fats, the type found in animal and dairy products and in tropical oils (palm and coconut), can cause health problems. Eating large amounts of food with saturated fats can raise the level of cholesterol in the bloodstream and increase the possibility of artery and heart disease. Unsaturated fats, the oils from vegetables and fish, are more healthful. Sugars are carbohydrates and are sources of energy for the body. They impart a sweet taste to foods. However, they are not especially important in our daily diet. An overabundance of sugars can cause weight and tooth decay problems. Other carbohydrates may be more nutritionally useful. Snack foods such as soda, candy, potato chips, and pastries are high in fats and/or sugars and should be a limited part of one's daily diet.

ENRICHMENT ACTIVITIES:
1) Find out about the various types of sugars found in milk, fruits, and vegetables.
2) Find out about unsaturated oils that are used in the preparation of fried foods.

ANSWER KEY:
Page 7–Transparency
1) Eating large amounts of fats and oils can lead to artery and heart disease. Excess sugars can cause weight and tooth decay problems.
2) Fruits, vegetables, and grain products are good low–fat and low–sugar substitutes.

Study Question: Saturated fats are those found in meats, dairy products, and certain tropical oils such as palm and coconut oils. They are usually solid at room temperature. Unsaturated fats are usually oils from vegetables and fish.

Page 7a
1) **high fat**—french fries, bacon;

high sugars—pastries, caramels, fudge

2) yogurt, ice milk
3) They have a sugar coating and are fried in fats.
4) potato chips, pork skins, peanuts (if salted)
5) fats are solids, oils are liquids; **fats**—shortening, lard, milk fats; **oils**—peanut oil, sunflower oil, olive oil

Page 8 *VITAMINS*

CONCEPT: Vitamins are nutrient compounds essential for growth and maintenance of normal body functions.

BACKGROUND INFORMATION: Experiments in the early 1900s with animals revealed that there were unknown essential factors in foods that improved an animal's appearance and growth. The lack of these factors caused poor appearance and growth. The compounds were identified with letters and thought to be amines essential for life (*vita* in Latin) and therefore given the name "vitamines." In 1920 it was discovered that the compounds were not actually amines and the final "e" was dropped. First found in butterfat, vitamin A is essential for good growth and for the health of the eyes. Although the vitamin is not found in plant foods, the body is able to convert yellow plant pigments into the vitamin. The vitamins of the B complex are compounds soluble in water. Lack of the vitamin results in serious nerve ailments. The B complex vitamins are found in both plant and animal foods. The disease of scurvy causes skin degeneration, sore gums, and hemorrhages. Naval physicians in the latter part of the 1700s learned that citrus fruits prevented the disease. The vitamin was isolated from lemons in 1932. Chemically, vitamin C is ascorbic acid and can be synthesized. The vitamin is necessary for wounds to heal properly and for the normal growth and integrity of bones and teeth. Vitamin D is found in milk, eggs, and fish. The vitamin is also made in the human body when certain compounds in the skin are exposed to sunlight. Lack of the vitamin causes softening of the bones and loss of muscle tone. Vitamin E is essential for the protection of red blood cells and the stability of cell membranes. The vitamin is found in both plant and animal tissues. Especially rich sources are vegetable oils, cereal grains, milk, butter, and liver. Vitamin K provides one of the necessary factors for blood clotting and wound healing. Leafy green vegetables are a good source. Some vitamins are also antioxidants, chemicals that prevent other chemicals from reacting with oxygen. This action can combat some types of cancer.

ENRICHMENT ACTIVITIES:
1) Find out about these diseases caused by vitamin deficiencies: beriberi, rickets, and pellagra.
2) Find out about health problems associated with taking too much of certain vitamins.

ANSWER KEY:
Page 8–Transparency
1) vitamin C
2) vitamin D

Study Question: When vitamins were first discovered, their chemical names were unknown so letters of the alphabet were used as names to identify them.

Page 8a
1) a. C, D; b. B; c. C, K; d. A; e. B; f. B, C, A
2) a. C; b. K; c. B, A, D; d. A, D; e. A; f. A; g. B, C, A, K; h. B, E
3) vitamins C and K
4) Bread, Cereal, Rice, and Pasta Group **or** Fats, Oils, and Sweets

Page 9 *MINERALS*

CONCEPT: Minerals are inorganic compounds that are essential for the regulation of many body processes.

BACKGROUND INFORMATION: A well-balanced diet provides the body with all the minerals necessary to maintain the body's processes and structure. Calcium and phosphorus are both required for the development, growth, and repair of bones and teeth. Calcium is also involved in the blood clotting process. Dairy products are good sources of calcium and phosphorus. Iron is the main component of hemoglobin in red blood cells. A lack of iron prevents hemoglobin production which can lead to anemia and its associated health problems. Iodine is a mineral found in seafoods. It is an additive to our table salt. Lack of this mineral can cause improper functioning of the thyroid gland. The result may be the formation of goiters and uncontrolled rates of chemical reactions within the body. A number of minerals are required in only very small amounts. Examples of these trace elements are magnesium, copper, zinc, sodium, and potassium. A complete lack of any one of these minerals can cause improper cell development, growth, and activity.

ENRICHMENT ACTIVITIES:
1) Research the relationship between iodine deficiency and goiter.
2) Find out about the role of zinc and chlorine in enzyme activity.

ANSWER KEY:
Page 9–Transparency
1) phosphorus, iodine
2) calcium, phosphorus

Study Question: Fluoride aids in the prevention of tooth decay; cobalt may have a role in preventing anemia; manganese functions in the metabolic process in which carbon dioxide is formed.

Page 9a
1) a. milk products, eggs, leafy green vegetables; b. Phosphorus; c. proper functioning of red blood cells, formation of vitamin A; d. seafoods, iodized salt
2) a. calcium and phosphorus, b. iron, c. iodine, d. calcium
3) calcium, phosphorus
4) By restricting the amount of salt put on foods and eating low–sodium foods.

Page 10 *THE DIGESTION PROCESS*

CONCEPT: The digestive system breaks down food into substances that cells can absorb and use. This system is also responsible for the elimination of unusable waste products.

BACKGROUND INFORMATION: The function of the digestive system is to transform complex, organic food substances into simple compounds that can be more readily absorbed by the body cells. Generally, food that is being eaten encounters the teeth first. The teeth function to hold, eat, and masticate the food materials. The materials are reduced in size. The tongue moves the material around, and the chewing process allows the food to become thoroughly mixed with saliva. There are three pairs of salivary glands that open into the mouth—the parotid, submaxillary, and sublingual. Their secretions moisten the food and add an enzyme which initiates the conversion of starches into sugar. After being moved to the rear of the mouth, the food mass is swallowed. The esophagus, a long muscular tube, receives the food and moves it along by a wave of rhythmic muscular contractions. The cardiac valve of the stomach controls the entrance of the food into the stomach, a muscular sac lined with a mucous membrane. The stomach receives the food and adds gastric juices containing enzymes and hydrochloric acid. As the food mass is being churned, chemical reactions take place. Complex proteins are changed into simpler compounds. The pyloric valve controls the release of partially digested material into the small intestine. The digestive juices of the liver, gall bladder, and pancreas are added. Bile from the liver emulsifies fats and oils. Its alkaline nature helps to neutralize the acid added in the stomach. Pancreatic secretions further the digestion of proteins, carbohydrates, fats, and oils. The small intestine adds secretions, and the digestive process continues as the food material moves along the tube. The main active material in the digestive juices are enzymes, proteins that act as catalysts. Small fingerlike projections (villi) of the inner surface of the small intestine greatly increase the absorptive surface area. Blood vessels within the villi take the nutrients and transport them throughout the body. The remaining material is moved to the large intestine, whose main function it is to consolidate the wastes by removing water. The rectum is the terminal section of the digestive tract. It functions to control the release of solid wastes through the anus.

ENRICHMENT ACTIVITIES:
1) Find out about the relationship between cholesterol in the bile and the formation of gallstones.
2) Find out how the food mass is moved through the digestive tract.

ANSWER KEY:
Page 10–Transparency
1) salivary glands, stomach, liver, gall bladder, pancreas, small intestine
2) the stomach

Study Question: The time varies, but usually takes from 18 to 30 hours.

Page 10a
1) A. teeth, B. tongue, C. liver and gall bladder, D. large intestine, E. rectum, F. salivary glands, G. esophagus, H. stomach, I. pancreas, J. small intestine
2) a. large intestine, b. salivary glands, c. gall bladder bile in small intestine, d. teeth, e. bile from the liver, f. rectum, g. stomach, h. tongue
3) Answers will vary. See Background Information above for major steps.

Page 10b
1) a. ptyalin, amylase; b. pepsin, trypsin; c. invertase, maltase, lactase; d. lipase
2) pepsin
3) liver via the gall bladder
4) small intestine
5) a. small intestine; b. salivary glands, pancreas; c. stomach, pancreas; d. small intestine, pancreas
6) Salivary glands in the mouth change the starch to sugar.
7) fatty acid and glycerol
8) They add moisture which makes the food mass easier to swallow.

Page 11 *CALORIES*

CONCEPT: The Calorie is a unit of measurement used to express the energy value of foods. Foods vary in the amounts of Calories they provide.

BACKGROUND INFORMATION: The calorie (small c) is a unit of heat measure defined as the quantity of heat necessary to raise the temperature of one gram of water one degree Celsius. A more usable unit to measure large amounts of heat energy is the kilocalorie—the Calorie (capital C). It represents the amount of heat needed to raise the temperature of one kilogram of water one degree Celsius. It is equal to 1000 small calories. The Calorie is often used to express the heat energy value of foods. An instrument called a bomb calorimeter is used to determine this heat energy value. A food sample is placed in a steel cylinder with oxygen under pressure. The cylinder is placed in a measured container of water. An electric fuse ignites the food–oxygen mixture. Explosive burning takes place. The rise in temperature of the water and the bomb give data from which the amount of heat given off can be calculated in Caloric units. In order for people to carry on life's activities, energy is required; foods furnish this energy. Not all foods supply people with the same amount of energy. The differences are due to the type of food (carbohydrates, fats, proteins) and the amount of indigestible material present. One gram of sugar or protein provides about 4 Calories; one gram of fat provides about 9 Calories. A Caloric intake greater than Caloric expenditure can result in the accumulation of fatty tissue.

ENRICHMENT ACTIVITIES:
1) Find out about the daily Calorie requirements for men and women and for the young and old.
2) Find out about sensible diet programs that plan Caloric intake.

ANSWER KEY:
Page 11–Transparency
1) Examples: apples, carrots, corn; 2) 450
Study Question: See Background Information.

Page 11a
1) carrots and apples
2) a. 260, b. 100, c. 280, d. 640, e. Answers will vary. Example: hot dog on bread, milk
3) a. pork chop, b. yogurt, c. peas
4) Answers will vary. Examples: Bread Group—slice of bread; Meat Group—chicken, boiled; Fruit Group—apple slices; Vegetable Group—corn; Milk Group—milk; total Calories = 505

Page 11b
1), 2), and 3) Answers will vary.
4) a. 2 hours, b. 7 hours, c. nearly 3 hours, d. 2 hours

Page 12 *GOOD NUTRITION*

CONCEPT: Good food choices for meals and good eating habits can help to maintain good health.

BACKGROUND INFORMATION: Many people in the United States have poor diets that do not meet the recommended standards of nutrition. This lack of good nutrition may be due to economic conditions or poor eating habits. There have been some noteworthy improvements in the food habits of United States citizens in the past several years. This is particularly true in the area of choices regarding foods high in fats, sugars, and salt. The work of school health and science programs has been a positive force in the dissemination of information regarding good eating habits. There are many sensible rules to guide people to better living and good health. One of these rules is to eat daily meals containing selections from each of the basic food groups, including more servings from the foods on the lower portions of the Food Guide Pyramid. It is also important to eat at regular hours, take time to sit down to eat and to chew foods well, and drink at least four glasses of water daily. An additional rule is to avoid foods that are high in fats, oils, sugar, and sodium.

ENRICHMENT ACTIVITIES:
1) Find out how cultural and social customs affect a person's eating habits.
2) Find out about the effects of insufficient quantities of water on a person's well–being.

ANSWER KEY:
Page 12–Transparency
1) milk, butter—Milk Group; toast, cereal, roll—Bread Group; berries—Fruit Group; potato, peas, parsley—Vegetable Group; pork chop—Meat Group
2) Nearly all body functions require water, and the major portion of cells consists of water.
Study Question: Fiber provides the bulk to help form and carry away wastes from the body. Insufficient dietary fiber may slow the passage of wastes through the colon and somehow be associated with high levels of colon cancer.

Page 12a
1) See Transparency 12 for answers.
2) The Food Guide Pyramid gives recommendations for numbers of servings from each food group to help ensure that people meet their daily nutritional needs.
3) a. blackberries, b. carrots, c. bran, d. tangerine, e. broccoli
4) Examples: potatoes, celery, cauliflower

Page 12b
1) 10%
2) yes
3) two
4) more sugars
5) vitamin A—yes, vitamin C—no
6) No. Forty percent of the Calories are from fat. The FDA recommends that no more than 30% of one's calories come from fat.

A Last Look—Part I

A. 1) Cheese does not belong. Macaroni and cereal belong to the Bread Group. Cheese is a dairy product.

2) Broccoli does not belong. Tuna and ham belong to the Meat, Poultry, Fish, Dry Beans, Eggs, and Nuts Group. Broccoli is a vegetable.

3) Pancreas does not belong. Pepsin and maltase are both enzymes. The pancreas is an organ of the digestive system.

4) Doughnut does not belong. Blackberries and bran are high–fiber foods; a doughnut is not.

OR

Blackberries do not belong. Bran cereal and a doughnut are both in the Bread Group. Blackberries are fruits.

5) Phosphorous does not belong. The stomach and esophagus are organs of the digestive system. Phosphorous is a mineral.

6) Yogurt does not belong. Peas and potato belong to the Vegetable Group. Yogurt is a dairy product.

7) Eggs do not belong. Butter and cheese belong to the Milk, Yogurt, and Cheese Group. Eggs belong to the Meat, Poultry, Fish, Dry Beans, Eggs, and Nuts Group.

8) Lipase does not belong. Calcium and iron are both minerals. Lipase is an enzyme.

9) Roast beef does not belong. Ham and bacon are both pork products. Roast beef comes from a steer.

10) Raisins do not belong. Rice and corn are both grains and belong to the Bread, Cereal, Rice, and Pasta Group. Raisins are a type of fruit.

B. 1) rice, fish
2) fruits
3) bread
4) meat
5) turkey, chicken, duck
6) milk
7) fish
8) yeast
9) fruits, vegetables
10) blackberries, peaches, or tangerines

A Last Look—Part II

A. 1) Milk, Yogurt, and Cheese Group
2) calcium

B. 1) Vegetable Group
2) vitamin A

C. 1) Meat, Poultry, Fish, Dry Beans, Eggs, and Nuts Group
2) iodine

D. 1) Fruit Group
2) vitamin C

E. 1) Bread, Cereal, Rice, and Pasta Group
2) niacin

F. 1) Meat, Poultry, Fish, Dry Beans, Eggs, and Nuts Group
2) vitamin E

G. 1) Meat, Poultry, Fish, Dry Beans, Eggs, and Nuts Group
2) vitamin A

H. 1) Bread, Cereal, Rice, and Pasta Group
2) thiamine

I. 1) Milk, Yogurt, and Cheese Group
2) vitamin D

A Last Look—Part III

A. 1) g   6) h
2) c   7) i
3) e   8) d
4) a   9) j
5) b   10) f

B. 1) blood   6) mouth
2) B   7) D
3) fiber   8) walking
4) Two   9) iron
5) more   10) sodium

A Last Look—Part IV

A. Answers will vary. Cartoon shows an exaggerated amount of iron. A magnet could not pick up the entire box of cereal.

B. 1) The egg should be circled. It is not a dairy product.
   2) The bread should be circled. It is not part of the Meat, Poultry, Fish, Dry Beans, Eggs, and Nuts Group.
   3) The pretzel should be circled. It is not rich in niacin.
   4) The corn should be circled. It is not a good source of vitamin D.

C. 1) cheese   3) orange
      butter   spinach

   2) pretzel   4) chicken
      macaroni   sardine

Food Guide Pyramid

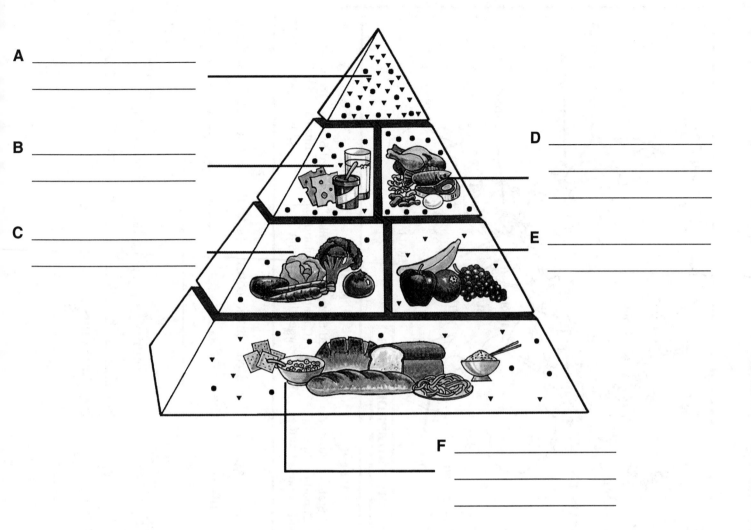

A _____

_____

B _____

_____

C _____

_____

D _____

_____

_____

E _____

_____

F _____

_____

_____

1. On the lines above, write the name of each food group and the number of recommended daily servings for each group.

2. What food groups are missing from this lunch menu?

        hamburger on bun   french fries   soda

_____

3. Before each food listed below, write the letter of the food group to which it belongs.

    a. _____ toast   f. _____ lima bean   k. _____ lemon

    b. _____ swiss cheese   g. _____ cauliflower   l. _____ cottage cheese

    c. _____ banana   h. _____ sardine   m. _____ ham

    d. _____ turkey   i. _____ pear   n. _____ shrimp

    e. _____ shredded wheat   j. _____ lettuce   o. _____ spaghetti

Major Food Producers

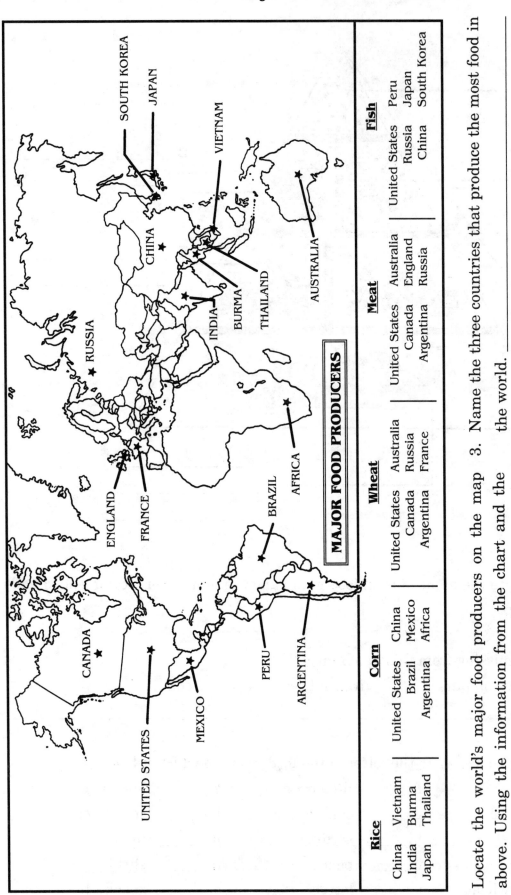

MAJOR FOOD PRODUCERS

Rice	Corn	Wheat	Meat	Fish
China	United States	United States	United States	United States
Vietnam	China	Australia	Australia	Peru
India	Brazil	Canada	Canada	Russia
Burma	Mexico	Russia	England	Japan
Japan	Argentina	Argentina	Argentina	China
Thailand	Africa	France	Russia	South Korea

1. Locate the world's major food producers on the map above. Using the information from the chart and the following symbols, show the food or foods produced in each country.

(R) rice $\triangle$ C corn $\triangle$ W wheat   M meat $\diamondsuit$ F fish

2. Name other grain crops grown in the United States. _____

3. Name the three countries that produce the most food in the world. _____

4. Asian countries produce large amounts of _____ and _____; non-Asian countries produce large amounts of _____, _____, and _____.

The Bread, Cereal, Rice, and Pasta Group

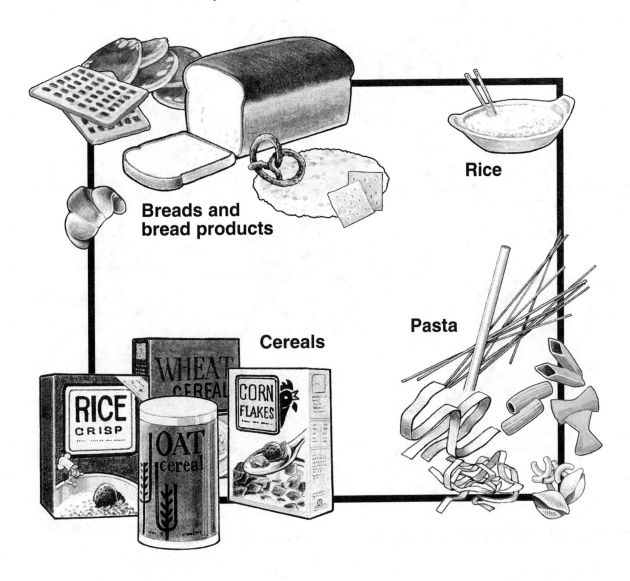

Breads and bread products

Rice

Cereals

Pasta

1. What other food items are made from flour? _____

   _____

2. Circle each food below that is **not** part of this group.

   a. wild rice   e. tortilla   i. muffins

   b. rye   f. tangerine   j. bran flakes

   c. potato chips   g. waffles   k. corn bread

   d. grits   h. buckwheat flour   l. raisins

3. List the food nutrients supplied to the body by this food group.

   _____

4. Name four pasta foods. _____

5. Why are so many servings per day recommended from this group? _____

   _____

The Fruit Group

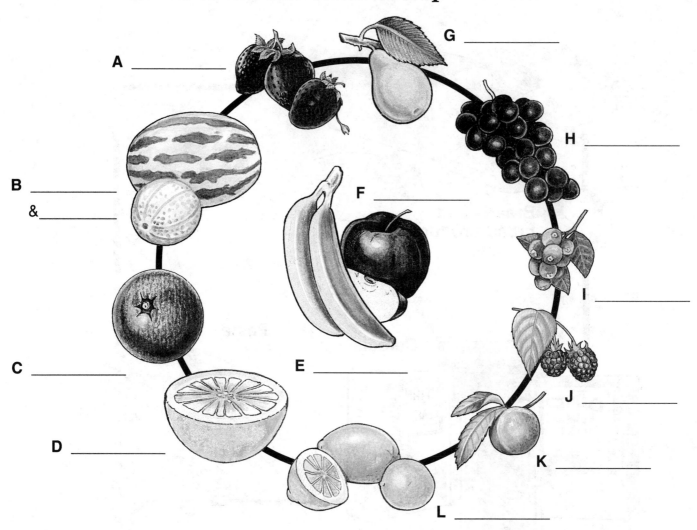

A _____

B _____
& _____

C _____

D _____

E _____

F _____

G _____

H _____

I _____

J _____

K _____

L _____

1. Write the name of each fruit on the line by its picture.

2. Identify which fruits grow on these plant structures.

    trees _____

    bushes _____

    vines _____

3. Which fresh fruits are used to make these food items?

    pies _____

    jellies _____

    juices _____

4. Name some other fruits not shown above. _____

    _____

The Vegetable Group

A _____

B _____

C _____

D _____

E _____

F _____

G _____

H _____

I _____

J _____

K _____

L _____

M _____

N _____

O _____

1. Write the name of each vegetable on the line by its picture.

2. Vegetables provide the body with these nutrients: _____

_____

3. Which vegetables are these plant structures?

    roots _____

    stems _____

    leaves _____

    flowers _____

    seeds _____

4. Name some vegetables that have large amounts of the following:

    starch _____

    fiber _____

The Milk, Yogurt, and Cheese Group

A _____

G _____

B _____

D _____

C _____

E _____

F _____

H _____

1. Label the foods of this group shown above.

2. Circle each food that is **not** part of the Milk, Yogurt, and Cheese Group.

   a. colby cheese   e. banana   i. frozen custard

   b. buttermilk   f. skim milk   j. orange juice

   c. popsicle   g. eggs   k. salad oil

   d. ice milk   h. cream cheese   l. tofu

3. Name the nutrients found in this food group. _____

   _____

4. How can you get the daily number of servings from this group, but avoid the fats?

   _____

   _____

The Meat, Poultry, Fish, Dry Beans, Eggs, and Nuts Group

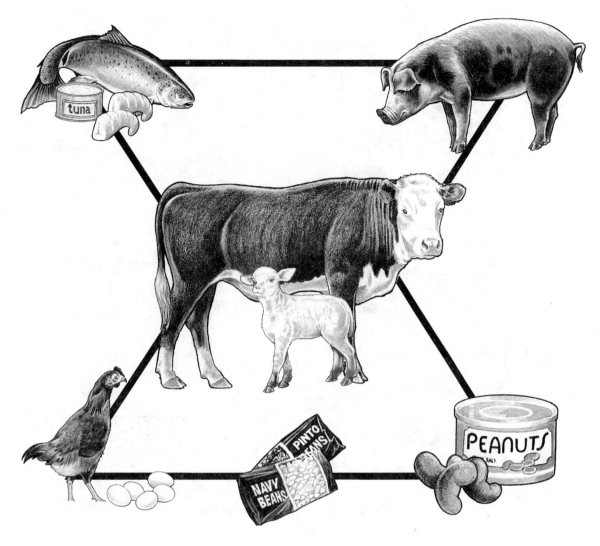

1. Name the animal that is the source of each of the following meat products:

   a. ham _____

   b. sirloin steak _____

   c. pork chops _____

   d. buffalo wings _____

   e. veal _____

   f. bacon _____

   g. hamburger _____

   h. hot dog _____

   i. mutton _____

   j. spare ribs _____

2. Give three examples of poultry. _____

3. Place a check mark before each of the following food items that belongs to this food group.

   a. ____ yogurt

   b. ____ pecans

   c. ____ shrimp

   d. ____ sausage

   e. ____ cheese

   f. ____ turnip

   g. ____ peanut butter

   h. ____ tuna

   i. ____ pickles

   j. ____ anchovy

   k. ____ dry beans

   l. ____ oysters

4. Name the nutrients provided by this food group. _____

   _____

Fats, Oils, and Sweets

1. Name other high–fat or high–sugar snack foods that are unhealthy if eaten regularly.

   _____

2. What frozen desserts can be substituted for ice cream? _____

   _____

3. Why are glazed doughnuts high in fat and sugar? _____

   _____

4. Foods high in sodium (salt) should also be avoided. Which of the above foods are also high
   in sodium? _____

5. What is the difference between fats and oils? _____

   _____

   Name some fats._____

   Name some oils. _____

Vitamins

VITAMIN	FUNCTION	SOURCES
Water Soluble **B complex** *thiamine, niacin, riboflavin, B_6 & B_{12}* **C**	growth, red blood cell production, healthy nervous system, release of energy from foods growth, wound healing, healthy bones and teeth	meat, eggs, milk, cereal grains, leafy green vegetables citrus fruits, tomatoes, leafy green vegetables
Fat Soluble **A** **D** **E** **K**	growth, good eyesight, healthy skin absorption of calcium and phosphorous by the bones and teeth stabilizes cell membranes, protects red blood cells blood clotting, wound healing	green and yellow vegetables, liver, fish liver oils, milk, yellow fruits milk, eggs, fish vegetable oils, eggs, cereal grains leafy green vegetables, egg yolks, tomatoes

1. Write the letters of the vitamins associated with each condition listed below.

    _____ a. healthy teeth _____ d. healthy skin

    _____ b. red blood cell production _____ e. healthy nervous system

    _____ c. blood clotting _____ f. growth

2. Write the letters of the vitamins associated with each of these foods.

    _____ a. citrus fruits _____ e. fish liver oils

    _____ b. egg yolks _____ f. yellow vegetables

    _____ c. milk _____ g. leafy green vegetables

    _____ d. fish _____ h. cereal grains

3. What vitamins are important for normal wound healing? _____

    _____

4. Name one food group that is not a prime source of vitamins A, C, D, and K.

    _____

Minerals

VITAMIN	FUNCTION	SOURCES
Calcium	bone and tooth development, blood clotting, muscle and nerve activities	
	bone and tooth development, normal cell activities	
Iron		
Iodine	for thyroid gland activity (controls rate of energy use)	
Magnesium *Copper* *Zinc* *Sodium* *Potassium*	traces necessary for proper body cell development, growth, and activity	present in small amounts in most foods

1. Complete the chart above by supplying the following information:

    a. List three food sources of calcium.

    b. Write the name of the mineral indicated.

    c. Describe the function of iron in the body.

    d. Name one food source of iodine.

2. Name the mineral or minerals important for proper:

    a. bone growth _____

    b. functioning of red blood cells _____

    c. thyroid gland activity _____

    d. blood clotting _____

3. Dairy products are a good source of which minerals? _____

    _____

4. Too much sodium (salt) in the diet can be harmful. How can you decrease the amount taken

    in each day?_____

    _____

The Digestion Process

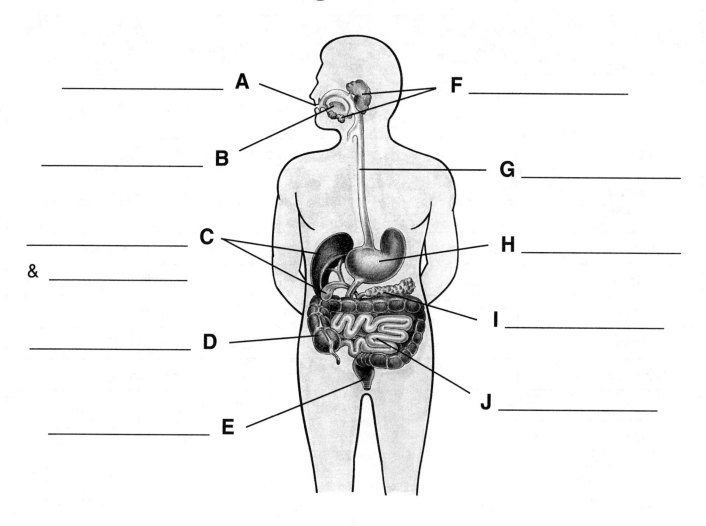

A _____

B _____

_____

& _____

_____

_____

F _____

G _____

H _____

I _____

J _____

C

D

E

1. Identify and label each part of the digestive system shown above.

2. Name the organ of the digestive system that performs each of the following functions:

    a. concentrates wastes _____

    b. secretions begin the conversion of starch to sugar _____

    c. absorbs digested food into the bloodstream _____

    d. reduces size of food particles _____

    e. secretions cause food mass to become alkaline _____

    f. controls elimination of solid wastes _____

    g. adds acid to food mass _____

    h. moves food around in the mouth _____

3. Briefly describe the major steps in the digestion process. _____

_____

_____

_____

Major Enzymes

ENZYMES	SECRETING STRUCTURE	FUNCTION
ptyalin	salivary glands in the mouth	begins conversion of starches to sugar
pepsin	stomach	changes complex proteins into simpler compounds
invertase (sucrase)	small intestine	complex sugars converted into simpler sugars
maltase	small intestine	changes maltose into glucose sugar
lactase	small intestine	changes lactose sugar into simpler sugars
lipase	small intestine	breaks fats into fatty acids and glycerol
trypsin	pancreas	continues digestion of proteins
amylase	pancreas	converts starch into glucose
lipase	pancreas, liver	changes fats into fatty acids and glycerol

1. Name the enzymes responsible for the digestion of:

    a. starches _____

    b. proteins _____

    c. sugars _____

    d. fats _____

2. Which enzyme functions in highly acidic conditions? _____

3. Where do the secretions that produce the alkaline condition in the small intestine originate?

    _____

4. In which organ does the conversion of sugars take place? _____

5. Name the structure that produces the enzyme to digest each of these foods:

    a. table sugar_____

    b. bread _____

    c. lean meat_____

    d. butter _____

6. Why does chewing on a starchy substance make it taste sweeter? _____

    _____

7. Name two products that are the result of enzyme action on fats._____

    _____

8. In addition to adding an enzyme, in what other way do the salivary glands function in the

    digestive process? _____

    _____

Calories

"Calorie" is the term used to express the energy value of foods.

CALORIC VALUES OF SOME COMMON FOODS

Food	Calories	Food	Calories
Apple, raw	70	Hamburger	260
Banana, raw	85	Ice cream (1 serving)	160
Bread, white (1 slice)	65	Malted milk (1 cup)	280
Candy bar, chocolate	250	Milk (1 cup)	150
Carrot, raw	30	Peanuts, roasted (1 cup)	840
Cheese, American (28 g)	115	Peas, cooked (1 cup)	110
Chicken, broiled (84 g)	115	Pizza, cheese (2 slices)	370
Cola drink	100	Pork chop (84 g)	300
Corn, cooked (1 ear)	70	Potato chips (10 chips)	100
Doughnut, cake	240	Taco	190
Egg, whole	80	Tuna fish, canned (84 g)	135
Hot dog	145	Yogurt (1 cup)	225

Study the chart above. Then answer the following questions.

1. Name two foods you could eat if you wanted a low–Calorie snack. _____

   _____

2. Approximately how many Calories would this meal have:

   a. hamburger _____   b. potato chips _____   c. malted milk _____

   d. **total Calories** _____

   e. What substitutions could you make to reduce the number of Calories in this meal?

   _____

   _____

   _____

3. Instead of the foods listed below, what item could you substitute in each food group if **more** Calories were needed?

   a. Meat Group—tuna fish _____

   b. Dairy Group—milk _____

   c. Vegetable Group—carrots _____

4. Design a balanced meal for dinner and determine how many Calories it contains.

   Bread Group _____

   Meat Group _____

   Fruit Group _____

   Vegetable Group _____

   Milk Group _____

Calories and Activity

ACTIVITY	NUMBER OF CALORIES USED PER HOUR
Seated—reading, writing, listening to a radio, watching television, eating	80 – 100
Slight—getting dressed or undressed, preparing meals, taking a shower, dusting furniture	110 – 160
Moderate—walking, doing carpentry work, working in the garden, making a bed, washing a car	170 – 240
Vigorous—walking fast, skating, bowling, scrubbing floors, playing softball	250 – 350
Strenuous—running, swimming, bicycling, aerobic dancing, playing tennis	350 or more

1. Record your activities for one day and the time it took to complete each of them. Use the table above to calculate the approximate number of Calories you used in one day. Record your total.

    Total Calories used: _____

2. Use a food Calorie chart to determine the amount of Calories you have taken in for one day. Record your total.

    Total Calories taken in: _____

3. Did you take in more or fewer Calories than you used? _____

    What happens when you take in more Calories than you use? _____

    _____

4. If you ate a meal with a total of 700 Calories, *approximately* how long would you have to do each of the following activities to use up those Calories?

    a. playing softball _____

    b. reading _____

    c. moderate walking _____

    d. bicycling _____

Good Nutrition

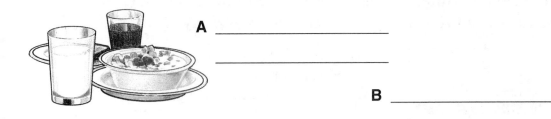

A _____

_____

B _____

_____

C _____

_____

D _____

_____

Foods with fiber form bulk—soft unabsorbed matter in the intestine—which is helpful in eliminating waste from the body.

Food	Amount	Fiber (grams)
Cereal, 100% bran	⅓ cup	8.4
Blackberries	¾ cup	6.7
Broccoli	½ cup	3.5
Carrots	½ cup	2.4
Peach	1 medium	2.3
Tangerine	1 large	2.0

1. In the appropriate blanks at the top of the page, write the good nutrition practices recommended for good health.

2. How is the Food Guide Pyramid related to good nutrition practices? _____

_____

3. Study the list of high fiber foods above and write the name of each food described below.

    a. _____ fruit with the highest amount of fiber

    b. _____ root vegetable that is high in fiber

    c. _____ cereal with a high amount of fiber

    d. _____ citrus fruit that is high in fiber

    e. _____ leafy vegetable with high fiber content

4. What other foods can you name that are high in fiber? _____

_____

Food Labels

Food labels required by the U.S. Food and Drug Administration (FDA) provide nutrient information to help plan a healthy diet.

Nutrition Facts
Serving Size 1 cup (243g)
Servings Per Container about 2

Amount Per Serving

Calories 100	Calories from Fat 10

% Daily Value*

Total Fat 1.5g	**2%**
Saturated 0g	0%
Polyunsaturated 0.5g	
Monounsaturated 0g	
Cholesterol Less than 5mg	**2%**
Sodium 450mg	**19%**
Total Carbohydrate 18g	**6%**
Dietary Fiber 3g	12%
Sugars 3g	
Protein 4g	

Vitamin A 60% (100% as Beta Carotene)
Vitamin C 0% • Calcium 6% • Iron 4%

* Percent Daily Values are based on a 2,000 calorie diet

Helps to make comparisons easier. Given in both household terms and metric units of measurement.

Indicates the number of calories from fat per serving. FDA guidelines recommend that no more than 30% of a person's calories should come from fat.

Provides information about nutrients most important for planning a healthy, nutritious meal.

Vitamin and mineral information

1. What percent of one serving of this product comes from fat?

   $$\frac{\text{total number of calories}}{\text{number of calories from fat}} = \% \text{ of fat} \underline{\hspace{5cm}}$$

2. Would this product be healthy for a person with heart disease? _____

   _____

3. How many people would this product serve for one meal? _____

4. Does this product contain more fats or more sugars? _____

5. Would this product be a good source of vitamin A? _____

   vitamin C? _____

6. A label on another food product lists the number of calories per serving as 150. The calories from fat are given as 60. Is this a healthy food? _____

   _____

A Last Look—Part I

A. In each of the following groups one item does not belong. Circle that item and in the space provided explain why it does not belong.

1.   macaroni   cheese   cereal

   _____

2.   tuna   ham   broccoli

   _____

3.   pancreas   pepsin   maltase

   _____

4.   bran cereal   doughnut   blackberries

   _____

5.   stomach   esophagus   phosphorus

   _____

6.   yogurt   peas   potato

   _____

7.   butter   eggs   cheese

   _____

8.   lipase   calcium   iron

   _____

9.   ham   bacon   roast beef

   _____

10.   corn   raisins   rice

   _____

B. Write the name of the food that will make each sentence a true statement.

1. Important foods in the diets of people in Asian countries are _____
   and _____.

2. Citrus _____ are good sources of vitamin C.

3. _____ is often referred to as the "staff of life."

4. Cattle, hogs, and sheep are animals that are commonly used as sources of _____.

5. _____, _____, and _____ are kinds of poultry.

6. Cheese, yogurt, and butter are derived from _____.

7. _____ is the best natural source of iodine.

8. Wheat, converted to _____, is found in many products of the bread and
   cereal group.

9. Good eating practices recommend that some raw _____ and _____
   be eaten each day.

10. _____ and _____ are fruits that are high in fiber.

A Last Look—Part II

On Line 1, name the basic food group of the food item shown.
On Line 2, circle the vitamin or mineral supplied in large amounts by the food shown.

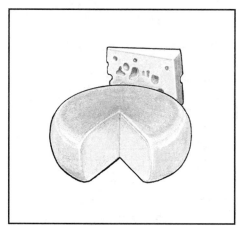

A. 1. _____

    2.   calcium   iron

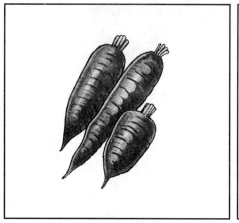

B. 1. _____

    2.   vitamin A   iodine

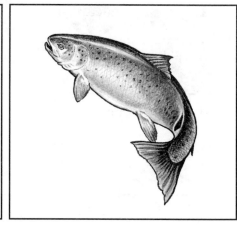

C. 1. _____

    2.   vitamin C   iodine

D. 1. _____

    2.   vitamin C   iron

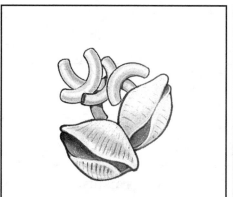

E. 1. _____

    2.   vitamin D   niacin

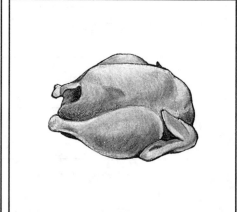

F. 1. _____

    2.   calcium   vitamin E

G. 1. _____

    2.   vitamin A   iodine

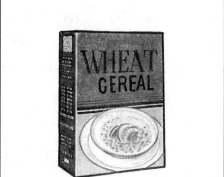

H. 1. _____

    2.   vitamin K   thiamine

I. 1. _____

    2.   vitamin D   vitamin E

Nutrition

A Last Look—Part III

A. Find the statement in the second column that best describes each word or group of words in the first column. Write the letter of the statement before the word it describes.

1. _____ meat
2. _____ Calorie
3. _____ small intestine
4. _____ B vitamin
5. _____ esophagus
6. _____ vitamin K
7. _____ large intestine
8. _____ iodine
9. _____ water
10. _____ vitamin C

a. riboflavin
b. food tube that connects mouth to stomach
c. measure of energy–producing value of food
d. necessary for proper functioning of thyroid gland
e. absorbs digested food into bloodstream
f. develops strong bones, teeth, and healthy gums
g. flesh of an animal
h. essential for blood clotting
i. concentrates wastes during the digestive process
j. non–food liquid necessary for good health

B. Circle the word or phrase that will make each sentence a true statement.

1. Vitamins E and K contribute to the proper condition and functioning of the _____.

      bones   blood   skin

2. Thiamine, riboflavin, and niacin belong to the vitamin _____ group.

      B   C   D

3. Bran cereal, blackberries, and broccoli are foods with high amounts of _____.

      seeds   calcium   fiber

4. _____ or more servings of fruits are recommended per day.

      Two   Three   Four

5. Roasted peanuts have _____ Calories than raw carrots.

      more   less   the same

6. Starch digestion begins in the _____.

      pancreas   mouth   stomach

7. Vitamin _____ is sometimes called the "sunshine" vitamin.

      A   D   K

8. Bowling uses up more Calories than _____.

      walking   running   swimming

9. Liver and molasses are rich in _____, which is necessary for the proper functioning of red blood cells.

      calcium   phosphorous   iron

10. Many fast–food items contain high amounts of _____.

      calcium   sodium   sugar

A Last Look—Part IV

A. Explain fully the meaning of this cartoon.

_____

_____

_____

_____

Wow! This cereal sure has a lot of iron in it!

B. There is something wrong with each of these drawings. Circle the part of the drawing that is incorrect and explain why you circled it.

1. _____   2. _____

_____   _____

3. _____   4. _____

_____   _____

C. Read each set of directions carefully before you write anything. Follow the instructions exactly.

1. Solve each puzzle to spell the name of a dairy product.

— — — — — — —

— — — — — —

🪑 – air + 🐑 – shp + 👟 – ho

🖌 – rsh + 🍞 – oas + 📷 – cama

2. Solve each puzzle to spell the name of a food in the bread and cereal group

— — — — — — —

🎁 – sen + 🍕 – piza + 🐪 – cam

🧲 – gnet + 🎂 – ke + 👲 – se + 🗡 – kfe

3. Solve each puzzle to spell the name of a fruit or vegetable.

— — — — — —

⛵ – 🦇 + 🚂 – ti + 🍇 – raps

☄ – wa + 🌧 – ra + ⌚ – wt

4. Solve each puzzle to spell the name of a kind of meat, fish, or poultry.

— — — — — — —

— — — — — —

🔧 – wren + ◯ – crle + 🐈 – itt

★ – t + 🦖 – osaur + 🍕 – pi